To my good + thoughtful
friend —
    John Ridley Finch
July 25, 1971

        Charles Milstead

MAN ON A SPACESHIP

The Meaning of the Twentieth Century Revolution
and the Status of Man in the Twenty-first and After

Man on a Spaceship

The Meaning of the Twentieth Century Revolution
and the Status of Man in the Twenty-first and After

by

William G. Pollard

Foreword by

Joseph B. Platt
President, Harvey Mudd College

§

The Claremont Colleges
Claremont, California

1967

Published by

CLAREMONT GRADUATE SCHOOL AND UNIVERSITY CENTER
for
The Claremont Colleges, Claremont, California

CLAREMONT GRADUATE SCHOOL AND UNIVERSITY CENTER
POMONA COLLEGE
SCRIPPS COLLEGE
CLAREMONT MEN'S COLLEGE
HARVEY MUDD COLLEGE
PITZER COLLEGE

Contents

Foreword

No one can foretell the future. Even the most imaginative and farsighted of the men of the mid-19th century—men like Jules Verne in technology or Admiral Mahan in naval strategy—saw only in dim outline a few features of the middle of the twentieth century. We now have a range of technology that would have astonished even Jules Verne and it is by no means clear to us what the shape of the mid-twenty-first century will be. We too may see some shapes, some outlines. That is what this book is about.

We do have some limited success in foretelling the future. Our most spectacular successes are in foretelling those events which can be described within our present knowledge of the laws of nature. The experience of the past is, of course, our only guide to the future, and for the past four centuries we have had a remarkably successful method for systematizing, testing, and reformulating those parts of our experience we can adequately control and repeat. We call this the scientific method. Once the laws of celestial mechanics were reasonably formulated two centuries ago, the planets lost their functions as ominous messengers of an inscrutable fate and became orderly parts of an understandable universe. From that time to this our knowledge of the natural world has grown through application of the scientific method, and we now find ourselves at home in a universe governed by laws, many of which we know and more of which we can discover. This new knowledge has enabled us to do a great many things we previously could not understand and hence not do. We are free now to move at will over the surface of the earth, the surface of the seas, and through the air. We are beginning to move into the depths of the ocean and of the earth's crust and into space beyond the air. We are increasingly familiar with our biological as well as our physical environment, and this understanding has enabled us to eliminate much of the ancient scourges of pestilence and famine.

One of the main features of the middle of the twentieth century is the extent to which the scientific method has enabled us to understand and to control the forces and the materials of nature.

But what is even more important to the human spirit is that we now believe that we live in an orderly world in which it is possible to understand and to plan. We may not be able to foretell the future, but we feel quite confident the events of the future will take place within the same laws of nature that govern our present experience. That conviction alone tells us a great deal about the future.

But not enough. The more we learn about nature the more we find there is still to learn, and we cannot make predictions with laws we have not yet discovered. Moreover, just as putting a jigsaw puzzle together is simple in principle but laborious in practice, some problems are just too much work. Even though we understand the rules for such a simple system as the motion of the air over the face of the earth, nature still operates a great deal more rapidly than we can calculate, and hence our calculations are of little help in predicting the weather. There are many areas in which either we do not know the appropriate laws of nature or else find their application too complicated for our use.

The laws of nature give us a great deal of help, but as we look toward the twenty-first century, we are particularly concerned with the actions of people. People are somewhat predictable too, which is why we have physicians and stockbrokers and why the third year of marriage sometimes proves boring. But these predictions lack the degree of certainty that we have come to associate with the "laws of nature." As far as we know, people act as if they made some choices unpredictably — that is, as if each person had a mind of his own and a measure of free will. To the extent that any man really has a choice, he is unpredictable. A better understanding of the laws of nature, including human nature, may enable us to make better and better predictions, but there is always the chance that our neighbor will exercise his own freedom of choice and do something we had not expected at all. There is the nagging possibility that improve as we may the methods of psychology, sociology, political science, and economics, we still may never know his mind completely, and there always will be the possibility of being surprised. If so, while we may be able substantially to reduce the uncertainties of the future, certainty will always be beyond our grasp. Furthermore, the greater the number of free people who are involved in shaping the future, the less certain that future becomes.

There is another way of dealing with the future, which is to assume—to take it on faith—that there is a purpose in human life and that enough of this purpose is available to us through the religious insights we inherit or can learn to enable us to choose between the uncertainties of the present with trust in the future. To those who hold this faith, the view into the twenty-first century is in some ways a strangely familiar view. It recalls, for example, a view across the Jordan three millenia back, and the Lord speaking through Moses to the children of Israel: "I have set before you life and death, blessing and curse; therefore choose life that you and your descendants may live."

During the last half of the nineteenth century, these two methods of dealing with the future were frequently in open conflict. During the first half of the twentieth century, except for certain rearguard actions, scientists and theologians have tended to be sufficiently busy with their own concerns to ignore each other. Many scientists have disregarded theology, and many theologians have disregarded science, on the grounds that anyone who was bright enough to understand that stuff ought to be wise enough not to bother. I have the impression that this period may be drawing to a close. There is a greater willingness for all to concede that the future holds uncertainties of such great import as to demand all the intellectual and the spiritual resources we can use to guide us in our choices. Within theology there is a greater willingness to restate the spiritual truths of our inheritance in terms that have meaning to a people who no longer believe in a flat earth with hell beneath and heaven above. Within science there is a greater willingness to concede that not all of truth is necessarily accessible to the methods of science. It is quite possible that these guides to action may be in some sense complementary so that the truths of one can neither be proven nor disproven by the methods of the other. We need theologians who are familiar with the content and the methods of science, and scientists who are aware of the concerns of theology.

William G. Pollard is such a man. Dr. Pollard is a physicist by his initial professional training. He earned his doctor's degree at Rice University and then joined the faculty at the University of Tennessee where he served for the period 1935-1947 with the exception of one year's leave of absence while he was working with the Manhattan District.

Over these years he taught physics and did research in the fields of cosmic rays, beta ray spectroscopy, and the behavior of gasses. In 1947 he became executive director of the Oak Ridge Institute of Nuclear Studies, in which capacity he was responsible for the initial nuclear training of many of the engineers and scientists who are now leading the development of peaceful uses of nuclear energy. The Oak Ridge Institute of Nuclear Studies was also instrumental in establishing a network of cooperative research agreements between the Oak Ridge National Laboratory and southern universities. Since 1966, Dr. Pollard has been president of the successor organization, Oak Ridge Associated Universities.

An active layman of the Protestant Episcopal Church, Dr. Pollard was ordained a deacon of that church in 1952. He read for orders and was ordained a priest in 1954. He served as a parish priest and as a priest associate. In addition to his scientific publications, he is the author of three prior books dealing with theological matters.

In this book Dr. Pollard brings both his science and his theology to bear on the uncertainties of our present time and on the shape of the twenty-first century. I commend it to your attention.

March 1967
Claremont, California

Joseph B. Platt

I

The Key to the
Twentieth Century

THE EARTH, in common with the other planets of the solar system and the sun itself, was formed by condensation out of a gravitationally collapsing cloud of gas and dust some 4,600 million years ago. Its history since that time has almost certainly been much richer than that of any of the other planets. It is probable that all of them initially had rather extensive atmospheres of hydrogen, ammonia, and methane, the same as those still retained by the major planets Jupiter and Saturn. During the first one or two billion years of the earth's history, the action of ultraviolet radiation from the sun on this atmosphere, combined with electrical discharges within it, produced free radicals of nitrogen and carbon with hydrogen. Reactions of these energy-rich free radicals with methane and ammonia then produced a variety of amino acids and other basic organic components of living systems. These processes must have occurred to some extent on all the planets in their early history.

1

Gradually the smaller planets, including the earth, lost their primordial atmospheres through escape of hydrogen from their gravitational fields. Through volcanic activity a great deal of water crystallization was released, and the earth acquired its oceans. As the oceans grew in volume, the organic materials produced out of its shrinking original atmosphere accumulated within them. The combination of these materials with phosphoric acid and dissolved ammonia in the primordial ocean produced in time, by processes not now understood, the elementary components of living systems. The earliest evidence of life that we have at present comes from the Gunflint Iron Formation on the north shore of Lake Superior near Schreiber Beach, Ontario. A chert in this formation, whose age is 1,900 million years, contains the fossils of many single celled microorganisms somewhat like modern algae. Thus cellular life had developed in the oceans two billion years ago.

Very slowly through photosynthesis these organisms replaced carbon dioxide in the atmosphere with free oxygen. In time the oxygen built up sufficiently to produce an ozone layer in the upper atmosphere which thereafter has effectively shielded out the intense ultraviolet radiation from the sun. As a result of this and other changes in the environment, the evolution of life took a new turn some 600 million years ago. Geologically the period is known as the Cambrian. In it the evolution of a variety of multicellular organisms was initiated and elaborated. The earth began to acquire a biosphere. By 300 million years ago the land was well covered with vegetation and populated by land reptiles and insects. In this period the great coal beds and oil fields of the earth were laid down.

Man in the form of our biological species *Homo sapiens* is one of the most recent to appear on the planet, arriving a mere thirty-five thousand years ago. During the first thirty thousand years he had very little effect on the balance of nature on the earth, over and above the effect which the introduction of any other new species had on it. The emergence of human civilizations, of cities and empires, literature and science, has all taken place in the last five thousand years. Even these developments, however, left vast areas of the earth largely untouched by man.

Our century, the twentieth, is unique in the whole history of our species on the planet, and indeed in the whole incredibly longer history of the earth itself. There is nothing in these previous histories to which it can be compared. We find ourselves in the midst of revolutionary changes of a magnitude and scope far beyond that of any other cataclysm which the earth has experienced throughout its billions of years. The purpose of these lectures is to interpret the character of this revolution, to examine its implications for understanding the phenomenon of man, and to foresee as far as possible its meaning for the future course of the histories of man and of the earth in the twenty-first and subsequent centuries.

A remarkably applicable key to these questions is found in a summary statement at the end of the first chapter of Genesis in the Bible. Although this chapter is based on the prevailing Babylonian cosmology of the fifth century B.C., the summary at the end of it relating to man is, as we shall see, remarkably applicable to our present concern. This summary occurs with considerable repetition in verses 26 through 28. "So," it begins by way of definitive summation, "So, God created man in his own image and blessed them and said to them: 'Be fruitful and multiply and fill the earth and subdue it; and have dominion over the fish of the sea, and over the birds of the air, and over the cattle, and over all the earth.'" This remarkable statement about man and his destiny in the earth has waited thirty-five thousand years to reach fulfillment, but is now with breathtaking speed being realized before our eyes. Only in the twentieth century has it been at all true of man's status on the earth. In it we can find a key to the meaning of the twentieth century.

All during the intervening twenty-four hundred or so years since this summation was written, it has not been really descriptive of man's status in the earth. Vast areas, even whole continents, of the earth's surface were only sparsely if at all settled by man. Man thought consciously of himself as a minority species among many other species. Human settlements were for the most part tiny islands in the midst or on the edge of vast forests or jungles in which the wild beasts held sway. He exercised a limited dominion over his own flocks of sheep, herds of cattle, horse, and dog. But always there was danger and uncertainty as ever-watchful tigers or wolves lurked in the shadows ready to pounce at the first opportunity. He exercised no dominion over two basic essentials, the world of microorganisms and the fertility of the soil. Pestilence, plague, and famine were ever-present threats periodically actualized in terrible scourges before which man stood helpless. Since he was bound to the earth's surface, the birds of the air remained beyond his reach. For all his cleverness as a fisherman and sailor, the sea remained vast and alien in which creatures large and small disported themselves oblivious of man and his ways. The dominion over the earth exercised by man was token and symbolic at best, and he was very, very far indeed from having subdued the whole earth to his purposes.

Man had been fruitful through previous centuries, but disease and famine prevented him from multiplying. At the beginning of the Christian era there were only about 300 million human beings on the earth. It required seventeen centuries to double this number to 600 million. Then in 1820, for the first time, the world population of species *Homo sapiens* passed the one billion mark. By 1930 it had doubled to two billion. Just a few years ago, in the early sixties, it passed three billion. By 1977 it will have reached four billion, by 1990 five billion, and by the end of this century, in the year 2000, it will be well beyond six billion, and the world will be just twice as crowded as it is now. Clearly our century, the twentieth, is the one in which the biblical injunction to be "fruitful and multiply and fill the earth" is at last being fulfilled. It is true of no other time in history. To us and to our generation the lot has fallen to experience the fulfillment of the purpose asserted for man when he began to inhabit this planet thirty-five thousand years ago; namely, that he should in the fullness of time multiply and fill the whole earth. It is a startling thought.

But the same century, the twentieth, marks the fulfillment of the rest of the injunction as well. There are many living today whose childhood was spent in the first decade of this century before the advent of either the automobile or the airplane, electric lights or appliances, radio or TV. In just the span of a single lifetime they have seen the whole face of the earth transformed by the phenomenon of technology. A jet flight over almost any part of the earth today provides striking evidence of this transformation. Everywhere the fields and highways, factories and cities of man stretch endlessly in every direction. The great primeval forests of the earth are rapidly shrinking and by the end of this century will have essentially disappeared. This is true not only of the developed portions of the earth — Japan, America, Europe, and Russia — but of those areas we consider underdeveloped as well — Asia, Africa, and Latin America. Even where the people continue economically depressed, technology in the form of steel mills and factories, highways and airports, dams, power plants, and machinery is everywhere in evidence. In this century man has not only filled the whole planet but he has subdued it as well and taken effective dominion over every creature.

In recent years wilderness and wildlife societies have been formed with a sense of panic about them. Even in Africa, which we still think of as a continent teeming with wild and exotic animals in a natural state, the true situation is one of the rapidly approaching extinction of many species. With the best that these societies, or any of us, can do, by the end of this century the only wild animals left on the earth will be found in zoos or scattered national parks maintained by man for their protection. All the rest of the planet will be devoted directly to man and his needs: to the production of his food and of the water and energy to do his work; his vast cities and the system of highways, air lanes, and seaways linking them together; his recreation and pleasures, foibles, fancies, and vanities. Occasionally he will visit a zoo or a wildlife preserve and

sense the pathos of a vanished world before man
took his God-given dominion over it, and feel a
sharp nostalgia for the earth as it was before man
filled it and subdued it. Over all the rest of the
earth every square inch of arable land will be devoted to human agriculture in which all that grows
and moves will be specially selected crossbreeds far
removed from the wild varieties which covered the
earth before man began to exercise his dominion
over them. All that lives will be especially suited to
the needs of man; any creature which fails to meet
this standard will be bred out of existence. Yet this
vast change in the status of living things on this
planet is the work of but a single century in the
whole 4,600 million-year history of the earth.

II

The Earth as a Spaceship

WE HAVE just thirty-three years to go in this century. It is a dreadfully short period in which to accommodate ourselves to the things which are so rapidly coming upon us, and to accomplish all that must be accomplished for man to continue his existence on the planet at any reasonable standard of living. In this brief period technological and social changes must somehow be achieved which dwarf in magnitude all others which have occurred in our past history and which have been accomplished over much greater time spans. It has become of the utmost importance for all of us to see as clearly as possible the character, direction, and challenges of the revolution through which the earth is passing.

The most effective image I have found for this purpose is based on recognizing that the earth is fast becoming a spaceship carrying mankind on a long journey through space. I am indebted to Kenneth Boulding for this image, which is partly developed in his important and stimulating book,

The Meaning of the Twentieth Century. Recently
the British economist Barbara Ward has employed
this same image most effectively in a book entitled
*Spaceship Earth.** Now that our astronauts completely encircle the earth in less than two hours, and
the rest of us can get jet flights to almost any part
of the earth in twelve hours, we have all come to see
the earth as small enough and compact enough to be
thought of as a spaceship. The atmosphere of the
earth is an ideal radiation shield, transparent to light,
but very effectively shielding us from the fierce ultraviolet, X-rays, and higher energy radiations of outer
space. In this the earth fulfills admirably one of the
primary requisites of a well-designed spaceship.

During its long prehuman history, the earth has
been prepared with a wealth of supplies now required by man, when he has filled the earth and
subdued it, to carry him on his long journey through
space from now on. Over long stretches of its geo-
logic history, the processes which have concentrated
ores of iron, copper, uranium, and other vital metals
have by now well stocked the earth with them for
man's requirements. Later in its history coal beds
and oil fields were laid down slowly over 100 million years to provide vast reserves of fossilized fuels
for man's utilization, primarily in the twentieth cen-

---

*Kenneth E. Boulding, *The Meaning of the Twentieth Century*
(New York: Harper & Row, 1965).

**Barbara Ward, *Spaceship Earth* (New York: Columbia Uni-
versity Press, 1966).

tury and after. It is as though some hidden designer had been at work for the last billion years or so specifically preparing the earth to become the spaceship for this creature who is now rapidly filling the earth and subduing it to his own uses.

There are several fundamental requirements for a satisfactory spaceship. First it must have an adequate source of energy which will last throughout the trip. Next it must have an adequate food supply or means of producing food for the crew throughout the journey. The air and water reserves in the ship must be kept pure and adequate for all needs. Wastes must be reprocessed or disposed of in ways which will not contaminate the ship. And, finally, the crew must not be allowed to increase in numbers, and it must remain unified throughout the journey. Divisions into warring rival subcrews or interpersonal conflicts between crew members would be catastrophic in a spaceship on an extended voyage.

All these elements of a spaceship economy face us in a particularly acute form as we move into the last third of this century. Consider first the basic requirements for energy and water. These are interrelated, and the key to both is nuclear energy. As we consider the vast requirements which face us in the immediate future, it seems remarkably providential that man should have stumbled on nuclear energy and the possibility of its controlled utilization less than thirty years ago. Although, spurred by the terrible threat of Hitler's Nazi Germany, it was first developed destructively, its discovery has come barely in time to make our continued occupancy of our spaceship possible.

Until only a dozen years ago, man was exclusively dependent on chemical energy (with the minor exception of hydroelectric power) derived from the burning of fossilized fuels, such as coal, oil, and natural gas, with the oxygen of the atmosphere. This form of energy is exceedingly rare, even esoteric, in the universe as a whole. There are very few spots other than the earth in the entire universe where the necessary ingredients for such energy can be found. Nuclear energy, on the other hand, is extremely common and universally present throughout all creation. Our sun is a natural hydrogen bomb in process of continuous explosion and so are the other so-called "main sequence" stars. Our galaxy, the Milky Way, contains some hundred billion such stars, and all the other galaxies are equally thickly populated with them. God has made more hydrogen bombs than he has anything else. There is nothing more common or more natural and universal in all creation. In the fullness of time it was inevitable that man in the fulfillment of the promise made at his creation would come to exercise dominion over this universal element of nature as well.

Most discussions of nuclear energy today seem to miss completely this natural character of it. Instead it is discussed as though it were a purely human invention, something introduced into the scheme of things by human technical ingenuity but not intended to be contained in the world as God prepared it for human habitation. Moreover, such discussions tend to concentrate almost exclusively on its destructive aspects, as though its only role in human affairs were that of placing upon man the terrible burden of our arsenals of nuclear weapons. Both of these views represent a dangerous distortion of the true situation. Hydrogen, lithium, thorium, and uranium are natural, pre-existent fuels just as much, if not more so, as are coal and oil. In the same way gasoline can be burned in a controlled manner to produce useful energy or made into napalm bombs for destructive purposes. Like everything else in nature over which man exercises dominion, he can exercise it either for a blessing or for a curse. This is the true status of nuclear energy.

The true role of nuclear energy for man becomes abundantly clear when we consider the post-revolutionary status of man on this planet in the twenty-first century. With the earth then supporting a total population in excess of seven billion human beings, we are forced to contemplate a radically different world from the one we knew before the revolution in the midst of which we now find ourselves began. To support such a population in a continuous and stable way will require an immense consumption of energy on a scale far greater than any we have seen so far. It will also require vast quantities of fresh water, mainly for irrigation of great desert areas of the earth not previously required for agriculture. Both the requirements for energy and for water can only be met with nuclear energy. We have already reached the danger point with water, and soon it is inevitable that we shall see more and more large nuclear-powered desalinization plants constructed along ocean shores all over the earth. Whether we burn the rocks (by extracting uranium for nuclear fission reactors) or burn the sea (by extracting deuterium for thermonuclear power plants), adequate reserves of nuclear fuels are available in the earth for many millenia. Coal and oil will be carefully husbanded and burned as fuel only for small mobile power systems, such as automobiles and airplanes. For electric power, desalted water, and space heating, nuclear power will be universally used. There is no other long-term alternative.

Thus by the end of this century nuclear power and sea water desalting plants will be commonplace in every country of the world. This is an essential requirement for the maintenance of the population which the earth will then be sustaining. Considerations such as these show how essential to human welfare it is that man should now be exercising his God-given dominion over nuclear fuels. In retrospect it is providential that the key discoveries which make it possible for man to use nuclear energy were made just when they were. Otherwise we would be facing the gravest problems of human survival on the planet for a period just a few decades away from the present. The blessing which man derives from his exercise of dominion over nuclear fuels is far greater and more crucial than has been generally realized. On the other hand, the corollary widespread distribution of nuclear fuels among all countries large and small is charged with terrifying possibilities. By the end of the century nuclear fuels are bound to be as common and universal as coal is now. In such a world *any* country large or small can fabricate these plentiful fuels into nuclear weapons at any time it wishes to. The problem of proliferation of nuclear weapons which so concerns us now will appear very different then. The specter of vast destruction in a nuclear holocaust can only grow more acute as time goes on. This too is an essential aspect of man's exercise of dominion over nature. We cannot have the possibility of blessing without the possibility of curse. Since it is man who exercises the dominion, it is man alone who determines whether it will be made a blessing or a curse. Hydrogen and uranium are inert. Like alcohol, dynamite, or morphine, they can be applied to either end by him who exercises dominion over them.

The need for water is closely tied in with the need for food. We are already running dangerously short of food for the world's explosively increasing population. The vast surpluses of grain and other staples which have plagued our agricultural system in this country for so many years are now gone. We will never see them again. Instead, restrictions on land under cultivation will be rapidly removed in the next few years, and the United States and Canada will be shipping greatly increased tonnages of grain and other foods to India, Pakistan, and China, and perhaps for several years to Russia as well. At the same time extensive increases in world fertilizer production which are already under way will be accelerated and the productivity of land in these countries which is already under cultivation will be greatly increased. All of these steps, however, will be adequate for not much more than another five years or so. To prepare ourselves for double the population at the end of this century, we must between now and then add an average of some thirty million acres of new land each year to that already under cultivation. Since most of this new land must come from desert areas of the earth's surface, we must arrange to supply it with about twenty billion gallons of fresh water per day, and we must add this much new water supply each year.

This is a staggering requirement, but we at Oak Ridge are convinced that it is now technologically feasible. The Oak Ridge National Laboratory has developed a prototype nuclear power reactor, the molten salt reactor, which promises to provide abundant energy at very low cost. The Laboratory is also the major center in the United States for research and development of nuclear desalinization plants. With very large-scale installations, it is technically feasible to produce several billion gallons of fresh water from the sea per day at a cost comparable to that for present irrigation water, with associated large-scale production of electric power at costs well below those of TVA today.

Nothing we do in nuclear desalinization of the sea will compare, however, with the evaporative power of that natural nuclear power plant, the sun. The action of the sun generates a known supply of 14 million billion gallons of fresh water per day which is twenty-five times the requirement of a world population of six billion people. This supply, however, is distributed very unevenly for agricultural purposes. To utilize even a small portion of it will require major engineering projects. One such project diverts three rivers in Australia which used to flow to the coast and into the sea through tunnels through the Snowy Mountains where they will irrigate arid valleys in the interior and generate two and a half million kilowatts of electricity in addition. In this country the diversion of the Colorado to the Los Angeles area, the Imperial Valley, and Mexico is under consideration, together with the huge Feather River project in northern California.

The most ambitious project of this sort would reverse the flow of rivers in northern Canada, which now flow into the Arctic Ocean, so as to provide 160 billion gallons per day to the western deserts of the United States and Mexico. Russia may in time reverse the flow of the Ob, the Lena, and the Yenisei rivers to supply tillable but arid regions there. Similar major projects are possible in China.

Given sufficient time, the dominion which man already knows how to exercise over the earth seems adequate, therefore, to provide food for a population of around ten billion people or even more. But the tragedy of the present decade is that we do not have time enough to carry out such projects before large-scale famines will set in. By 1970 famine of catastrophic proportions seems inevitable in India, Pakistan, and China. It will be a calamity unparalleled in human history, involving death by starvation for numbers running into the hundreds of millions. We have somewhat longer in South America, but, unless major projects can be initiated in the next few years, famine of comparable proportions will occur there by 1980. These are some of the realities of our filling the earth and trying to achieve the means in such a short time to subdue it and convert it into our spaceship. In the long run, say thirty or forty years, we have the technological means to provide enough food. But the immediate needs are so pressing and are increasing so rapidly that there seems no possibility of avoiding short-term catastrophe.

Another spaceship requirement which is already becoming crucial, particularly in the United States, is the necessity for adequate reprocessing and disposal of all wastes. Air pollution, particularly in Los Angeles and New York, has become a problem already of crisis proportions. The pollution with industrial and human wastes of our rivers and lakes has reached such levels that vigorous national programs of control seem to be imminent. In another ten or twenty years, however, the same problems will plague the whole earth. Rapid world-wide industrialization will soon persuade all nations that this is a planetary, not a local, problem. The earth is a single spaceship with a single atmosphere and single water system. With a population over double that presently on the earth, waste reprocessing and pollution control will have become recognized planetary necessities requiring a world-wide system of controls.

Here again the technological means for achieving adequate control of atmospheric and fresh water purity are either available now or seem assured in the next ten years. Most of the industrial effluents now fouling our rivers and lakes could be processed with equipment already on the market to recover and process chemicals and pay off the initial capital investment in three to ten years. Air pollution from industrial and utility plants can be similarly controlled, although at some additional cost. In time fuel cells or improved rechargeable batteries must replace gasoline for automobiles and trucks. The whole problem is now more political and economic than technical. Its solution threatens deeply intrenched interests and firmly established patterns, and so will be accompanied by considerable social and political stress and strain. But the ultimate demands of a spaceship economy will in time force a solution.

These problems of energy, water, food, and waste handling arise from and are created by the explosive increase in human population which is now going on. As we have seen, in the remaining third of this century man will have fulfilled the biblical injunction to be fruitful and multiply and fill the earth. But an inescapable corollary of this injunction faces us now with terrible urgency. Because the earth is in fact a spaceship for man's journey, it is essential that once the earth has been filled by man, he must stop being fruitful and cease further multiplication. Moreover, this must be accomplished within a generation, or certainly within no more than two generations. The children of today's college graduates must, as they approach adulthood, already have started the process which their children must complete; namely that of separating human sexuality from procreation. All over the world this process will involve a profound religious and moral readjustment. Yet there is no viable alternative to such a transformation. What God required of man during the long centuries before he filled the earth is quite different from what He will require of man after he has done so. This seems clear enough. Once the crew of the spaceship has reached its full complement, there is an absolute requirement that it not be allowed any further increase. Yet no other requirement calls for such a deep-seated readjustment in long-established religious, moral, and social patterns, or is more resolutely resisted by mankind.

This problem of achieving a stable human population on the planet dwarfs all others in both urgency and difficulty. Yet one way or another it must and will be achieved. I am fearful that only after famines of awful proportions and their accompanying social paroxysms will sufficient pressure have been brought to bear to force men to a solution. But there is no other way out. In the end sometime in the twenty-first century, and hopefully early in the century, a stable planetary population will have been achieved at somewhere between six and ten billion human beings. When this has been done the requirements of that population for energy, fresh water, food, and pure air can and will be met, although most of the intellectual energy and scientific and technological skill of humanity will be absorbed by this task.

The last, and certainly the most difficult problem in achieving a satisfactory occupancy of our spaceship, is the requirement of unity in the crew. It is to this aspect of the problem that Barbara Ward's book, *Spaceship Earth*, to which we have already referred, is devoted. When we consider the vast social and political problems which presently confront mankind, the ultimate unification of man on the planet which must somehow be achieved seems almost unattainable. There are radical conflicts in ideology dividing the world into two vast armed camps. As we crowd closer together on the earth the way must, and, I feel confident, will be found for holding these ideologies in some kind of creative balance. Other tensions arising out of deep historic hurts maintain local conflicts in the Middle East, Southeast Asia, among African tribes, and elsewhere on the earth. America and South Africa are powder kegs of racial tension between white and black. Doubtless the achievement of what Barbara Ward calls a "balance of ideology" will involve paroxysms along the way of an intensity greater than any we have so far known. But each will, I believe, bring us closer to that unity which our spaceship status requires. Each of these adjustments will involve, as Miss Ward so fully describes, a move toward a "Balance of Power" and a "Balance of Wealth" in addition to the balance of ideology. All represent drastic changes in the world of warring nation states, of haves and have-nots, which we know now. Yet her searching analysis of all these problems does lead to a kind of guarded optimism about the ultimate outcome.

III

The Creation of Man

THE SUMMARY statement about man which we have been using to understand our present situation begins with the assertion that "God created man in His own image." Before we can consider the prospects for the future of man in the twenty-first century and beyond, it will be well to pause and consider the meaning which can be given to such a statement in a modern context. This is necessary because it is widely believed today that the statement is untrue. Rather than having been created, it is said, man has evolved in the same way as all other species. The process of evolution can, it is thought, be understood mechanistically in terms of biological variation through mutations coupled with natural selection in a changing environment. As to the remainder of the statement, the prevailing conviction is that man creates his gods in his own image rather than the reverse.

In the immediate post-Darwinian period the great emphasis was on man's continuity with the rest of life in the total evolutionary process. Man was brought down from his pedestal and exhibited as just one more species of animal among many that had come and gone. In one sense, this was an entirely necessary emphasis called forth by the widespread revolt against such an idea in non-scientific circles. Coupled with it was a tendency to vastly oversimplify the steps leading to man. These steps were looked for among present-day primates so that a sequence from monkey to great ape to man was postulated. Currently the tendency is more and more to emphasize the discontinuities and the explosive character of man's evolution. The steps leading to him were very much more complex than was originally thought. Modern monkeys and apes are the result of parallel evolutionary strands in which many of the steps leading to them, as with the steps leading to man, no longer exist.

The long geological history of the earth's crust has been punctuated every 100 million years or so by violent releases of accumulated energy from radioactivity deep beneath the crust. These crusted revolutions, technically called "orogeny" by geologists, result in throwing up new ranges of mountains with associated volcanic activity. Such periods involve abrupt climatic changes and other radical changes in the environment. One of the more recent of these, called the Laramide revolution, ushered in the age of mammals seventy million years ago. This revolution threw up the Rocky Mountains in North America, the Antilles in Central America and their continuation in a corresponding range running through Venezuela and Colombia. The extremes of climate caused the dinosaurs and many other species to become extinct at the end of the Mezozoic era in what has been called the "age of great dying." It was followed by a long period of mild climate called the Tertiary, during which the mammals evolved into the great variety of species we know today.

Among the mammals, an evolutionary development took place during the Tertiary which started with a group of small animals something like the lemurs and tarsiers of today. This development produced the primate stem of mammals, and it took place along three independent lines in South America, South Africa, and Malaysia. Then at the end of the Tertiary another period of orogeny, called the Cascadian revolution, began, which brought that epoch to a close. This was only two million years ago, and we are still in the midst of this revolution. It has produced the Cascades and the Sierra Nevadas in this country, the Andes in South America, and the Alps and Himalayas in Europe and Asia. This period is called the Pleistocene, and it has been marked by radical changes in the earth's climate, including four ice ages, the formation of large desert areas, extensive volcanic activity, and other severe environmental changes compared to which the Tertiary was calm and unperturbed.

At the beginning of the Pleistocene the evolution of primates in Africa, no doubt accelerated by the environmental trauma of the age, took a fateful turn for the whole subsequent history of the earth. Like all else in its beginnings, the roots of this new direction are invisible. But silently, almost stealthily, man was introduced deceptively as though he was to be just one more species among the many being developed and introduced into the already teeming life in the great forests and wind-swept steppes of the Pleistocene. Pierre Teilhard de Chardin describes the scene at the end of the Tertiary on the eve of this fateful event:[*]

> *A great calm seems to be reigning on the surface of the earth at this time. From South Africa to South America, across Europe and Asia, are fertile steppes and dense forests . . . . And amongst this endless verdure are myriads of antelopes and zebras, a variety of proboscidians in herds, deer with every kind of antler, tigers, wolves, foxes, and badgers, all similar to those we have today . . . . Except for a few lingering archaic forms, so familiar is this scene that we have to make an effort to realize that* nowhere *is there so much as a wisp of smoke rising from camp or village.*

The first evidence of man appears just at the beginning of the Pleistocene two million years ago in

---

[*]Pierre Teilhard de Chardin, *The Phenomenon of Man* (New York: Harper & Row, 1959), p. 152.

southern Africa in barely human form as the species *Homo habilis*. This rather bestial primate, only a little more man-like than ape-like, did have the broad pelvis and upright posture characteristic of his successors on the human stem. For the next million and a half years he evolved and diversified in such a way that in time two principal groupings or branches became discernible. One of these, called the *Australopithecines*, represents an evolution away from man toward less and less human traits. The other branch evolved toward man in a diversity of forms which became more and more man-like as time went on. There are numerous fossil remains of both types which have been found in southern Africa.

One of the developments in the second branch of *Homo habilis* represented, by the time he became numerous enough about 300,000 years ago to be detectable in fossil remains, a leap forward in the development of man. He is called *Homo erectus*. He had a larger body and a somewhat better shaped jaw with less prominent teeth than his *Habilis* precursor. He had an easier upright posture and bipedal walking, and his freed hands assisted by a more ample brain allowed him to make crude stone implements and to use fire. As soon as he became numerous enough, the *Australopithecines* and other varieties of *Homo habilis* became extinct, unable to compete with him. Moreover, he migrated widely out of Africa into Europe (Heidelberg man) and Asia, and his remains have been found in China (Sinanthropus) and Java (Pithecanthropus).

Then about 100,000 years ago a new development occurred out of the steady biological diversification of *Homo erectus*. He is called Neanderthal man and many fossil remains of him showing a considerable variety in form and structure have been found. He was skillful at making tools and weapons and at fire building, and for the first time he buried his dead. But he had a low forehead with thick orbital ridges, protruding heavy jaws, and short thick arms and legs. If we could see a member of *Homo neanderthalis* today, we would not consider him human at all, even in comparison with the most primitive bushmen. Nevertheless his great superiority over *Homo erectus* left the latter powerless to compete with him, so that he became extinct soon after the appearance of Neanderthal man.

Then suddenly, even explosively, modern man appears on the scene about thirty-five thousand years ago out of one of the developing strains within *Homo neanderthalis*, who then rapidly disappeared, helpless in competition with this new creature. He appears just as the ice is retreating from Europe after the last ice age. Biologically he had a large brain capacity made possible by a soft cranium at birth followed by a very rapid growth of head and brain and a greatly increased blood supply to the brain.

His skull was high with straight wide forehead, flattened face, well formed chin, and agile arms and hands. He is *Homo sapiens,* and he is obviously one of us. He suddenly arises before us all over Africa, Europe, and Asia, complete and modern, and yet already so complex as to be divided into the principal races of modern man wherever his remains are first found. He not only made tools and buried his dead, like his predecessor, but he learned to make fires from scratch with frictional heat, rather than simply preserving a fire obtained from a natural source. Moreover, an inner life, barely hinted at in Neanderthal burials, now overflows into artistic expression in drawings, paintings, and carved objects. How delighted we still are with the pictures he left on the walls of caves in southern France of mammoth and reindeer, and of men wearing animal skins as clothing and heads as masks!

Against the background of this rather brief and hurried sketch of the appearance of man as it is currently understood, let us return to our question about the creation of man. There are several ways we can approach this problem with some hope of insight into it, and I shall take them up one at a time. But first we must consider the meaning of the word itself. If by "creation" we mean something logically contrary to "evolution," then certainly man is not created, since the evidence for his evolution is overwhelming. On the other hand, when we use this word of a human agent, rather than of God, as when we speak of a creative artist or of human creativity in general, we always have in mind a process rather like evolution. Man's creativity expresses itself in some great sculpture, painting, piece of literature, symphony, or mathematical theorem through slow and often labored processes working on more or less intractable materials. Human creativity is always the product of the human imagination and genius operating within the processes of nature and using the materials nature provides.

In contrast to this, whenever we speak of God as creating, we most often have in mind an act whose only human analogy would be a magician pulling a rabbit out of a hat, or a rub of Aladdin's lamp bringing into being a castle fully equipped with servants, food, and wine. Creation in this sense is certainly the antithesis of evolution. Yet what, other than the general context of an imprecise pre-scientific world view, commits us to such a picture? Indeed if, as I shall try to show in the next chapter, it is proper to say in any significant sense that man is created in the image of God, then why are we not forced to the alternative of seeking to understand divine creativity from what we know of human creativity, since one is the image of the other?

With this thought in mind, a striking feature of the evolution of man is its similarity to the production of a great literary masterpiece. A great piece of literature goes through several drafts, with the earlier drafts destroyed when the new ones are completed. It is a continuous process, yet there are discontinuities of new inspiration and expression which mark off the several drafts from each other. So it was with man. If we think of *Homo sapiens* as a great literary achievement like Shakespeare's *Hamlet,* then *Homo neanderthalis, Homo erectus,* and *Homo habilis* are like successively earlier drafts of the final version, all of which were destroyed when each new draft was completed. If we try to understand the masterpiece in terms of its earlier versions by tracing it back through successive drafts, we lose it; it escapes from us. So too it is with man. There is no first man; no Adam and Eve. Rather, as when we trace a great river to its origins, we end with a tiny stream which disappears into the ground at its source, so when we trace man back through the neanderthals to the early habilis primates, we lose him. He disappears gradually into something which is not man.

This analogy between man and a piece of literature can be given remarkable substance in terms of the great breakthrough in biology of the past decade. We know now that all life on this earth is written in a common language with a common alphabet. The letters of the alphabet are a selected set of twenty chemical substances called "amino acids." The number of compounds known to chemists as amino acids run into the hundreds. Living systems contain some eighty of them. Yet only twenty are used in the alphabet, in the same way that human languages arbitrarily select from twenty to thirty letters out of a large number of possibilities to form an alphabet. With this alphabet words are written which form a class of compounds known generally as "proteins." The complete spelling of many of these words, such as hemoglobin, insulin, and a number of enzymes and hormones, is now known, and new ones are being determined in increasing numbers. All life on this earth, from viruses and bacteria to trees, flowers, fishes, and men is written in this same language with this common alphabet.

Closely associated with this "language of life" is the means by which living systems store and transmit the information required for writing it. This system is a very ingenious coding system using four coding symbols, which is remarkably like the punched tapes used to give instructions to a modern electronic computer. The master code, of which each cell has a complete copy, is a nucleic acid called DNA. Copies of portions of this master code, used to direct the writing of specific words, are made from it with another nucleic acid called "messenger RNA." Triplets of coding symbols on messenger RNA are specific for one of the twenty amino acid letters. These letters are attached to short strands of RNA called "transfer RNA," of which there is one type specific for each letter. The code on the messenger RNA is read off by different transfer RNA's lining up opposite their appropriate three symbol codes and inserting their amino acid letters in order so as to produce the proper spelling of the protein word.

Each living organism is a kind of poem written in this protein language. The process of evolution is one in which the master DNA codes have been slowly elaborated in the quantity and variety of information impressed upon them through spontaneous changes or mistakes in the code called mutations. Interacting with the associated environmental changes accidentally occurring in synchronization with these mutations, the process of natural selection continually weeds out errors and misspellings and capitalizes on new and novel possibilities. A scientific examination of the process shows how the language is written, the grammatical rules for its construction, and in general the machinery which underlies its utility as a language suitable for the expression of great ideas. Such a description of the evolutionary process stops, however, with the chances which govern mutations and the character of the environmental changes which accidentally couple with them.

The creativity of evolution manifests itself in the great and beautiful ideas which somehow get expressed as DNA codes thread their way through such a manifold maze of chance and accident. One could imagine in theory a complete description being achieved of the daily interplay of chance and accident as it affected step by step the organisms of the whole earth from the unicellular microlife in the sea two billion years ago up to the present time. Such a description would show how step by step the DNA codes had been elaborated over that immense length of time so as to lead from such microlife to the ultimate achievement of man. But it would in no way *explain*, except by way of saying that an incredible number of chances capitalizing on a continuously varying environment not causally related to them, had in fact accomplished so remarkable a result. It could not say whether the remarkably diverse literature which has been produced in the language of life was creative or not. Creativity is an inner aspect of the externally observable steps by which the creative result is achieved. This applies to a building like the Taj Mahal or a book like *Alice in Wonderland* just as much as it does to the production of man in the evolutionary process.

Another quite different way to approach the question of man's creation is based on the question raised by the possibility of men on other planets. There is a widespread conviction, reflected in science fiction, that once life gets started anywhere in the universe it will inevitably evolve into man-like creatures. The most elaborately argued statement of this viewpoint is in Walter Sullivan's* recent book, *We Are Not Alone.* The completely unscientific character of such a view is most fully set forth in a book by the eminent biologist and evolutionist George Gaylord Simpson.** In a chapter entitled "The Nonprevalence of Humanoids" he says in part:

> *Both the course followed by evolution and its processes clearly show that evolution is not repeatable. No species or any larger group has ever evolved, or can ever evolve, twice. Dinosaurs are gone forever. Nothing very like them occurred before them or will occur after them. That is so not only because of the action of selection through long chains of nonrepetitive circumstances . . . It is also true because in addition to those adaptive circumstances, there is a more or less random element in evolution involved in mutation and recombination . . . Repetition is virtually impossible for nonrandom actions of selection on what is there in populations. It becomes still less probable when one considers that duplication of what are, in a manner of speaking, accidents is also required. This essential nonrepeatability of evolution on earth obviously has a decisive bearing on the*

---

*Walter Sullivan, *We Are Not Alone* (New York: McGraw-Hill, 1964).

**George Gaylord Simpson, *This View of Life* (New York: Harcourt, Brace and World, 1964), p. 267.

chances that it has been repeated or closely paralleled on any other planet.

The assumption so freely made by astronomers, physicists, and some biochemists, that once life gets started anywhere, humanoids will eventually and inevitably appear is plainly false. The chance of duplicating man on any other planet is the same as the chance that the planet and its organisms have had a history identical in all essentials with that of the earth through some billions of years.

There is in fact an impressive test of this conclusion in the history of the evolution of primates on the earth. No two planets could be any more alike in environment and the sequence of environmental changes than are South America and Africa here on the earth. Yet under these very similar environments the evolution of the primates took very different directions on these two continents. In South America it has produced the family of new world monkeys. Until man migrated to South America from Asia there was nothing at all like him there. There is every reason for believing that no amount of subsequent evolution of the small and agile primates of this continent would ever have led to man. If there is another planet anything like earth on which life has evolved, is it not reasonable to ask whether the course of evolution would have followed that of

Africa or of South America, or some other totally different path? The latter is of course most likely. But in any event the planet could as easily miss producing man as South America did here.

The anthropologist Loren Eiseley concludes a similar analysis of this widespread conviction about the inevitability of man evolving from elementary forms of life with the following passage:*

> *Lights come and go in the night sky. Men troubled at last by the things they build, may toss in their sleep and dream bad dreams, or lie awake while the meteors whisper greenly overhead. But nowhere in all space or on a thousand worlds will there be men to share our loneliness. There may be wisdom; there may be power; somewhere across space great instruments, handled by strange, manipulative organs, may stare vainly at our floating cloud wrack, their owners yearning as we yearn. Nevertheless, in the nature of life and in the principles of evolution we have had our answer. Of men elsewhere, and beyond, there will be none forever.*

Now that we know that it is possible to use molecules to code vast amounts of information in a reliable, reproducible, and exceedingly dependable

---

*Loren Eiseley, *The Immense Journey* (New York: Random House, 1957), p. 162.

way, there is no reason to believe that some similar coding scheme with an associated language has not been devised long ago or will not be far in the future on many other planets throughout the universe. But the language in which life is written on them and the literature developed in that language would doubtless be as different as are Hebrew and Chinese in our own history. This is what is implied in the assertion that life, and in particular, man is a creation. The creation of one *Hamlet* in any literature does not require or call for its duplication in any other. The possibilities in any literature for new creations are unlimited. Exalted expressions of the spirit as great as or greater than man may well have been produced or are now in preparation elsewhere in the universe; but not a duplication of man himself.

IV

The Image of God

No educated modern man can escape the simple conclusion that he is an integral part of nature like everything else he sees about him. He is composed throughout of the same atoms as the distant stars and the rocks beneath his feet. The same DNA code that produces the cockroach and the thistle produces him. He is written in the same language with the same amino acid alphabet as all other life around him. He evolved in the same evolutionary process as mice and rats, his dog and his horse, and he has a common origin with them far back near the beginning of the Tertiary. He has lost his sense of uniqueness in the scheme of things, a uniqueness which he used to interpret before this drastic change in outlook was forced upon him by understanding himself to have been created in the image of God. Such an assertion he believes to be no longer tenable.

Yet in spite of this evident continuity with everything else about him, there remains in man much which has no parallel with anything else he knows in nature. His imagination and thoughts; his self-awareness and freedom; his memories, anticipations,

39

and anxieties; his aspirations which by persistence of will accomplish so many remarkable things; and above all most recently his mathematics, science, and technology. How is he to understand himself as an integral part of nature, and yet possessing such attributes which he finds nowhere else in nature? Above all, now that he finds himself exercising complete dominion over all the rest of nature on the earth and in process of converting the whole earth to his spaceship, does this not point to a uniqueness which he perhaps never suspected in himself before?

There are profoundly paradoxical elements in man's status in the total scheme of things. When we examine the way in which man was produced, the most striking thing about the record is man's complete continuity with all that came before him. We cannot put our finger on any specific point which separates man from non-man. It would be so much easier to understand ourselves if in going backward we could come upon an Adam and Eve. Instead biologically and anatomically there is a continuous progression toward man which moves slowly for the most part, but is interrupted now and then by brief periods of rapid and decisive change. Compared to other primates, *Homo habilis* is already human. But compared to twentieth century man he is much more an ape than a man. Somewhere in between a really decisive change must have taken place, even though it is not very evident biologically and anatomically.

In my own approach to this problem I have not found any better way to locate this point of decisive change and to understand its significance than to say that with the appearance of *Homo sapiens* thirty-five thousand years ago there had at last been produced, in the long evolutionary process, a creature whose uniqueness is best described by the assertion that he alone among all the manifold other species of life is made in the image of his creator. With the appearance of *Homo sapiens* came an overflowing of the inner life into artistic expression witnessing to imagination, thought, and perhaps play which was indeed something entirely new on the earth. Without realizing it at that time, this new creature already possessed the capacity to fill the earth and subdue it and take dominion over everything else on it. As soon as he appears, the remains of Neanderthal man disappear, swept away by the superior prowess of *Homo sapiens*. Perhaps before him one could have said of Neanderthal man that he came closer than any other creature ever had to reflecting something of the image of God. But had the creative process ended with him, there would have been no literature or art, no science or technology, and thus no dominion. With *Homo sapiens* we know at the outset we are dealing with the imagination and spirit which makes all of this ultimately possible. With him God has at last elaborated DNA codes in the long evolutionary process to the point of bringing into existence a creature made in His image.

In its ultimate significance for the future of the whole earth, the step to *Homo sapiens* is seen in retrospect to have been an immense discontinuity in the history of life. Teilhard de Chardin expresses this point forcefully in his *Phenomenon of Man*:[*]

> . . . *how utterly warped is every classification of the living world in which man only figures logically as a genus or a new family . . . To give man his true place in nature it is not enough to find one more pigeon-hole in the edifice of our systematisation or even an additional order or branch. With hominisation, in spite of the insignificance of the anatomical leap, we have the beginning of a new age. The earth 'gets a new skin.' Better still it finds its soul . . . This sudden deluge of cerebralisation, this biological invasion of a new animal type which gradually eliminates or subjects all forms of life that are not human, this irresistible tide of fields and factories, this immense and growing edifice of matter and ideas — all these signs that we look at, day in and day out — seem to proclaim that there has been a change on the earth and a change of planetary magnitude.*

---

[*]Teilhard de Chardin, *op. cit.*, pp. 182-183.

In order to properly express the planetary scope
of the phenomenon of man, Teilhard de Chardin
introduces the term *noosphere.* Just as the bio-revo-
lution which separates the pre-Cambrian from the
Cambrian in the history of the earth can be described
as clothing the earth, beginning 600 million years
ago, in a "biosphere," so the introduction of a new
species, *Homo sapiens,* a mere thirty-five thousand
years ago has resulted in clothing the earth in a
noosphere; a sphere, that is, which glows all around
the earth with a phosphorescence of thought, imagination, and spirit. Teilhard derives this word from
the Greek stem "nous" for mind in the same way
that biosphere is derived from the Greek stem for
life. The impact on the planet has been just as fundamental and just as revolutionary in each case. As the
divine energy worked through the chances and accidents of evolution to develop the full florescence of
the biosphere over the earth, we know that God
looked upon the teeming blanket of life which began
to clothe the earth and saw that it was good. Now
just recently when he clothed the earth in its noosphere at the point when *Homo sapiens* emerged
from *Homo neanderthalis,* we can almost hear Him
saying: "Let us make man in our image, after our
likeness, and let them have dominion over the fish
of the sea, and over the birds of the air, and over the
cattle, and over all the earth."*

---

*Genesis 1:26

To assert that the introduction of a single new species has resulted in the conversion of the earth's biosphere into its noosphere is to assert a uniqueness and a discontinuity for that species which far transcends the minute biological and anatomical changes which differentiate it from those which preceded it. In a very real sense the existence of the noosphere is the manifestation on a planetary scale of the image of God which the members of the species bear. The phosphorescence of thought and spirit which now blankets the earth is one of the most striking testimonies to this remarkable fact about man.

We are indebted to modern science for an entirely new insight into the question of the extent to which we can interpret man as bearing the image of God. I am indebted for this insight to a fascinating paper by a winner of the Nobel prize in physics, Eugene P. Wigner, with the title "The Unreasonable Effectiveness of Mathematics in the Natural Sciences." The main point of this paper is to comment on the numerous occasions in the history of physics since Newton in which a mathematical system, originally a pure product of the human mind, has subsequent to its development proved remarkably applicable to an accurate description of nature. Since nature is certainly not itself a product of the human mind, the correspondence between the mathematical system and the structure of things in the natural world has a kind of miraculous quality about it. It is not something we would ever have anticipated in advance, and it is a fact which escapes our understanding.

The first instance in which the truly amazing character of this correspondence confronted mankind was the combination of second order differential equations with the remarkable properties of quantities which vary inversely as the square of the distance from a point. This combination constitutes Newton's formulation of the law of universal gravitation and of the motion of bodies under it. Of this Wigner says:[*]

> *Philosophically, the law of gravitation as formulated by Newton was repugnant to his time and to himself. Empirically, it was based on very scanty observations . . . The law of gravity which Newton reluctantly established and which he could verify with an accuracy of about 4% has proved to be accurate to less than a ten thousandth of a per cent and became so closely associated with the idea of absolute accuracy that only recently did physicists become again bold enough to inquire into the limitations of its accuracy.*

Another miracle of this sort left an indelible impression on the great physicist Albert Einstein, who first experienced it in the development of his Gen-

---

[*]Eugene P. Wigner, "The Unreasonable Effectiveness of Mathematics in the Natural Sciences," *Communications on Pure and Applied Mathematics,* XIII (1960), pp. 1-14.

eral Theory of Relativity. Well before he undertook this task, a very beautiful general mathematical theory of multidimensional curved spaces had been developed by Riemann, Christoffel, and a number of other mathematicians. The theory was expressed in tensor form, which makes the geometrical properties of the space independent of any particular choice of coordinate system in which it is expressed.

Einstein's objective was to see if it was possible to define a four dimensional space-time geometry in such a way that its curvature would eliminate the force of gravity. In such a curved space-time, bodies would follow geodesic curves, like airplanes flying great circle routes on the earth, and so would behave as though not acted on by any force. In order to accomplish this it would be necessary to relate the curvature of space-time to the distribution of matter. Large masses would curve space-time around them more strongly than small masses. For this latter problem, the most general description of an arbitrary distribution of matter in motion which conserves energy and momentum leads to a symmetric tensor of ten components. What Einstein required then was a symmetric tensor involving only the geometric properties of the four dimensional space-time, which when equated to the tensor defining the distribution of matter would lead to ten equations. Solutions of these ten equations would then describe the motions of bodies in any type of gravitational field. What he

found was that in the Riemannian geometry of a
four dimensional space there was only one symmetric tensor of the right properties and that this tensor
had indeed just the required ten components! It was
all or nothing. There was one and only one possibility for a correspondence between the mathematical
system in the mind of man and the distribution of
matter in the natural world. Yet it led to a set of
gravitational field equations whose solutions do in
fact correctly and accurately describe the way bodies
in nature move under the influence of each others'
gravity.

The discovery that a completely formed product
of the human imagination and reason like the Riemann geometry of a four-space should later prove to
uniquely and accurately describe the structure of a
natural world whose only relation to the human
mind is through the process of Darwinian evolution
which produced it is nothing short of amazing. Yet
this same miracle has happened in even more as-
tounding ways since.

The great mathematician David Hilbert had developed early in this century a very beautiful mathematical theory of spaces in which all lengths are
complex numbers.* Such a space is called a Hilbert
space. Well after the full development of this theory,
physicists in trying to understand the spectra of

---

*A complex number has the form $x + iy$ where x and y
are ordinary numbers and i stands for $\sqrt{-1}$.

atoms found that a remarkably general description of atomic systems can be obtained if the physical states of atoms are represented by vectors in a Hilbert space of infinite dimension and if all their observable physical properties are represented by Hermitian operators in that space and their average numerical values by the Hermitian scalar product. The theory based on this kind of representation is called quantum mechanics. The successes of quantum mechanics in the diversity of cases and unfailing accuracy with which it describes molecules, atoms, and nuclei is truly amazing. Yet, as Wigner points out, complex numbers are neither natural nor simple and are never seen in any direct observation of nature. A complex Hilbert space of infinitely many dimensions in which Hermitian scalar products can be formed seems a pure fabrication of the human mind as far removed from the natural world as it would be possible to get. To then discover, as we have, that the whole intricate substructure of nature conforms accurately and in every detail with the mathematical properties of such a space is nothing short of a great miracle. Wigner comments on this miracle with the following conclusion to his paper:[°]

The miracle of the appropriateness of the language of mathematics for the formulation of the laws of physics is a wonderful gift which

---

[°]*Ibid.*, p. 14.

we neither understand nor deserve. We should be grateful for it and hope that it will remain valid in future research and that it will extend, for better or for worse, to our pleasure even though perhaps also to our bafflement, to wide branches of learning.

It is impossible to appreciate the force of these considerations without having personally experienced the amazing ways in which the theories of mathematical physics apply to the natural world. I have a feeling that most physicists have become, through too much familiarity, insensitive to the really amazing and miraculous character of the correspondence which they live with and practice every day. Yet the structure of matter and of space and time was established long before man appeared on this planet equipped with a brain which seemingly is only the accidental product of the operation of natural selection on chance mutations in a changing environment. Yet now we have discovered that systems spun out by that brain, for no other purpose than our sheer delight with their beauty, correspond precisely with the intricate design of the natural order which predated man and his brain. That surely is to make the discovery that man is amazingly like the designer of that natural order. How better describe this discovery than to assert that man is indeed made in the image of God!

These considerations suggest that we have come something of a full circle in our attitudes toward the phenomenon of man. In the pre-scientific era, man thought of himself as distinct and separate from nature. The assertion about him that he was created in the image of God seemed obvious to him and entirely in accord with his general view of the world. Then came Darwin and the growing realization that man was the product of exactly the same process which had produced all other living things, and that he was as much an integral part of nature as stars and rocks and trees. This seemed to deny both his creation and even more emphatically that he bore anything of the divine image. Indeed for some time there seemed to be no evidence for any involvement of God either with man or any other part of nature.

Now, however, with a more thoughtful view of divine creativity in the light of what we know from human creativity, the whole evolutionary process shows striking evidences of creativity; or, better perhaps, in no way precludes an interpretation that it has been creative. Moreover, from the perspective of the mid-twentieth century, we are able to see two very fundamental aspects of the phenomenon of man which would not have been evident before. One of these is the conversion of the biosphere into the noosphere. The other is the miraculous correspondence between the fabrications of man's mind and the inner design of nature, as evidenced by the applicability of abstract mathematical systems to the laws of nature in physics. Both of these quite new perspectives strongly support the contention that man is after all made in the image of God. What we have come to realize is that there is no scientific reason why God cannot create an element of nature from other elements of nature by working within the chances and accidents which provide nature with her indeterminism and her freedom. We also see in a new way that the fact that man is indeed an integral part of nature in no way precludes his bearing the image of the designer of nature. Or to put it another way, there is nothing to prevent God from making in His image an entity which is at the same time an integral part of nature.

V

The Future of Man

The most general statement we can make about the future is that it is quite unpredictable. From our present vantage point there is no way to picture just what the state of the world will be at the end of this century in the year 2000. At no time in the history of man has the future presented him with such unimaginable possibilities for catastrophe nor at the same time with such immense opportunities for human advance. Which of these possibilities or opportunities will be actualized, and in what combinations and sequences they will occur during the next thirty-three years we cannot now know.

Yet at the same time we can perhaps identify certain broad features and trends in our present situation which should play a major role in shaping our future history on the planet. Some of this has already been done in the second chapter in terms of the requirements of a spaceship economy. Short of complete catastrophe in a universal nuclear holocaust, there are certain fundamental requirements for energy, clean air and fresh water, food, and fertility control which must and will be met. They are elementary requirements for the crew of any spaceship.

The physical means for meeting these requirements are either in hand or in sight. It is only the social and political elements which are uncertain. My own guess is that by the mid-seventies major water desalinization, irrigation, air pollution, and agricultural engineering projects will be in full swing all over the world. By the mid-eighties population and fertility control measures will have become a major worldwide effort, and the social and moral adjustments attendant on this effort will be in an acute phase. Beyond these two convictions, I must confess to considerable haziness as to what the near future holds.

In the social-political arena we are least able to penetrate the veil of the future. There are strong evidences of a growing rapprochement between the West and the USSR as well as its Central European satellites. It seems to me that this kind of drawing together is inevitable as nations become more highly industrialized. The management requirements and social structure of any highly advanced technological society are determined largely by the technology itself. As a result, all countries reaching this stage of development become very much alike regardless of professed differences in ideology. This in time will be true of China. But until such a stage is reached, China will become increasingly, and probably throughout the remainder of this century, the storm center of world politics. The most ominous ele-

ment in the China situation for the ultimate achievement of the unification of mankind on the planet is
the underlying racial tension with its terrible fore-
boding of a major conflict between Asia and the
West. A division of humanity into oriental versus
occidental could be catastrophic, and every effort
should be made to ameliorate this source of tension
and to forestall any developing conflict along such
lines.

The period since the close of the second World
War has been marked by the rise of nationalism.
Considering the spaceship economy toward which
we are moving with such rapidity, the continued
creation of new nation states inexperienced in gov-
ernment and each carrying a burden of antagonisms
and bitterness deeply rooted in history is one of
the greatest threats of the immediate future. Yet
paradoxically this same period has been marked all
over the world by a vigorously growing allegiance
of individuals to mankind as a whole in opposition
to national allegiances. The paradox is brought out
sharply in a whole spectrum of programs like the
Peace Corps, American Field Service, scientific and
cultural exchanges, agricultural missions, and the
like, which involve close personal relationships between diverse peoples all of whom are motivated
by supra-national loyalties. These trans-national relationships have been developing at an ever-accel-
erated pace beneath the surface of international

politics. In contrast to this, the diplomatic relations of nation states have continued to be carried out on an official level above the surface in the traditional spirit of national rivalries and ambitions. It is difficult to foresee just how the balance of forces between these contending elements of the contemporary scene will change as the history of the remainder of this century unfolds.

It is of special interest to speculate on the future development of the two primary elements in the shaping of Western civilization, namely, Christianity and science. Here I am sure that my own expectations differ considerably from generally accepted opinion. I shall discuss these expectations in reverse order, together with such reasons as I am able to advance in support of them.

The mid-twentieth century has certainly been the golden age of science. Most scientists who express themselves on the subject foresee an indefinite extension of this age into the future. They point out how misguided certain scientists were at the end of the last century who believed that the scientific description of nature was essentially complete. They then go on to assert that the possibilities of further scientific discovery are essentially unlimited and that we can look forward to a never-ending pageant of scientific wonders. Such forecasts generally receive wholehearted and enthusiastic public support from the nonscientific segment of society. Although I share the enthusiasm for science and the delight in its remarkable achievements which prompt such expectations, I have serious reservations about their validity.

My first reservation is based on the present state of science itself. In the physical sciences the frontiers on which really new discoveries can be expected have already been pushed to the point where productive research requires very massive and expensive equipment. These are the areas of sub-nuclear or particle physics, which require for their further exploration very-high-energy accelerators costing hundreds of millions of dollars to build and some $50 million or more annually to operate. From the nuclei of atoms up through various states of matter to the boundary of high temperature plasmas, the general outline of our understanding is well established. Research in this domain will continue indefinitely at a sustained level to improve and refine our understanding. But no one foresees any revolutionary new discoveries in this domain of nature. At its upper boundary of high temperature plasmas, there may be new and unsuspected phenomena to be uncovered. But again increasingly expensive equipment is required here also for significant new research. The only other frontier in the physical sciences is astronomy in which entirely new phenomena may still be discovered in distant galaxies. But again large scale and expensive optical or radio equipment or even more expensive earth satellite observatories are required. For the remainder of this century all of these areas will be pushed, but certainly at a rapidly diminishing return in new knowledge per million dollars of investment in securing it.

The really scintillating field of research for the remainder of this century will be in the biological sciences. Here the recent breakthrough in deciphering the genetic code and recognizing life as a language insures a growing frontier of new knowledge and a variety of unsuspected new discoveries which will be exciting indeed. Moreover, compared to the frontiers in physical science, this field is inexpensive. What it calls for rather is the imagination and individual genius which has been the mark of science in the past. However, after thirty-three years of exploitation of molecular biology at the present level of effort, my guess is that it too will have reached a declining rate of new discovery per unit of effort expended.

All these considerations suggest to me a gradual transformation of the character of science during the remainder of this century. It will slowly lose the dynamism and zest of the age of exploration and new discovery which has characterized it in the previous third of the century. More and more it will be devoted to working out an increasingly refined and sophisticated understanding of what is already known. At the same time, while this transformation of the inner character of science is going on, the external role of science as the means for man's dominion over his spaceship earth will increase greatly in importance. Applied science and technology will become even more than they are today the absolute essential for man's continued habitation of the planet. Requirements for energy, water, unpolluted air, food, and fertility control will grow insistently and frightfully in the next decade. More and more all of our spare resources and intellectual energy for scientific and technological effort will have to be directed to the insistent demands for meeting these requirements.

Sending men to the moon and bringing them back in 1969 may prove to be from the perspective of the twentieth century the central symbol of the golden age of science in the twenty-first. Like the great pyramids of Egypt or the lofty cathedrals of medieval Europe, this feat will stand out as a peak expression of the spirit of a golden age; the maximum economic investment which a great civilization could make in a feat which served no useful purpose other than making manifest the lofty height to which the spirit of an age could rise. It will not be worth repeating except perhaps by Russia for the purpose of sharing in its glory. Thereafter, even more massive applications of science and technology to basic human needs will have become so urgently necessary that no further diversion of available talent and resources to manned space flights can be permitted. Instrument flights to Venus, Mars, and other planets should and will continue, however, because of the very interesting and valuable scientific information obtainable from them.

If history has any lesson to teach us, it is that golden ages do not go on indefinitely. They have their own inner structure of expression and achievement which once attained leads to a slow decline in the vitality and dynamism which produced them. So it will be too with the twentieth century golden age of science. By the twenty-first century, science will have simply taken its essential place as the servant of the spaceship economy which will then prevail. There will be even more science then, and it will be even more important for society than it is now. It will, however, have become routine and taken for granted. It will no longer constitute as it does now the dominating passion and excitement of an age to the near exclusion of all other expressions of the human spirit. At least this is the way I read the signs of the times.

The dominating passion for science and the heady excitement of at last achieving the dominion over nature promised to man at his creation, which have made the twentieth century the golden age of science, have brought with them a corresponding decline in religion. The twentieth century has been uniquely marked among all others in the history of man by an all-pervasive secularism. In its passion for subduing the earth, the spirit of the age has rejected all religion as being irrelevant to its task. Doubtless the passion for science with its brilliant series of discoveries opening up so dramatically our understanding of nature, coupled with the excitement of participation in a revolutionary age in which man has taken dominion over the whole earth have made such a single-minded concentration on the here and now inevitable. Doubtless also a number of other factors in a complex pattern have entered into shaping the structure of ideas which characterize the age. But whatever may be the reason for the phenomenon, we see the evidence for it on every hand.

In Europe and America the twentieth century has seen the disappearance of Christendom as the primary cultural phenomenon of Western civilization, and the resulting alienation of the Church from the dynamics of contemporary history. Religion continues to have a certain emotional and psychological appeal, and it retains some hold through the carry-over of traditional social structures and practices. But religious categories are by now completely absent from contemporary modes of understanding man, his history and destiny, and his relation to the universe. In Russia and China the complete secularization of life and society is an official policy of the State and a basic tenet of the philosophy which supports that policy. In Africa all of the new nation

states are engaged in a wholesale abandonment of
their past histories and traditions, along with religion, in order to plunge headlong into the twentieth
century with its passion for science and its promise
of dominion. The result of all this has been a planetary tide of secularization before which all religion —
Christian, Jewish, Moslem, Hindu, Buddhist, and
Confucian — is rapidly shrinking. By the end of the
century it seems to me almost certain that none of
the great religious institutions which have informed
and inspired all the human civilizations of the past
3,000 years will play any significant role in the new
planetary society which will then clothe the earth.

Having said this, however, I must hasten to add
that I also confidently anticipate a renaissance of
rediscovery of the religious dimensions of reality
which will be well started by the end of the century.
Partly this expectation arises out of the character of
modern science itself. The prevailing secularism of
our time is largely a heritage of nineteenth century
science. In the meantime modern physics has re-
covered much of the sense of mystery which its
earlier versions were so bent on dispelling. It has
become quite natural to think of the whole order of
nature, the sum total of objects and events in three
dimensional space and time, as immersed or im-
bedded in a larger invisible reality. The recovery of
a real sense of an external reality transcendent to
the order of nature, so essential to all religion, will

accompany the spread to society at large of the new spirit of modern science.

By the twenty-first century man's dominion over the whole earth will no longer be something still in process of achievement, but something already accomplished by earlier generations in the preceding century. The earth will already have been filled and subdued by man. From then on man's chief endeavor will be to accommodate himself to the fact of this situation, and apply his energies as best he can to stabilize the new world society to a spaceship economy organized for an endless trip through space. In such a situation the passion for this world and its conquest by man which marks us, will have given way to a growing concern with the purpose and meaning of existence. The all-pervading secularism which characterizes our age will no longer be relevant in such a changed situation. Questions about the meaning of man, his origin and creation, the extent to which he bears the image of his creator, and his relation to transcendent reality and to eternity will gradually become dominant again. There will quite certainly be a renaissance for religion in the years ahead.

In all of this, I have tacitly assumed that man will make it through the remainder of the 20th century, and that there will be a world of some sort in the next century about which we can try to make predictions. This may well be an overly optimistic view. Man is certainly at a cross-roads in his long history. Not only for himself but for the frail vessel of which he is the captain, he holds the power of blessing or of curse, of life or death. There is much in the contemporary scene to suggest that he may well be choosing the curse instead of the blessing and that we are rapidly heading toward the destruction of both man and his planet.

As we view the vast challenges of the last third of this century, many shrink from the prospect of confronting them. It is easily possible to despair of man's capacity to pass through such an unprecedented period of his history, or ever to achieve the essential requirements for his spaceship voyage. Kenneth Boulding indeed finds much cause for pessimism about the present predicament of man. An even more gloomy picture is painted by the eminent anthropologist, Loren Eiseley. In a recent book, *The Firmament of Time,* he expands on a theme he developed earlier in a paper bearing the title, "Man, the Lethal Factor," in which the creation of man on this planet is seen as a vast cosmic error. For all of its 4,600 million-year history, the earth had been moving to ever-increasing beauty, loveliness, and wealth in the elaboration of its biosphere. But with the appearance of man a deadly, lethal factor is introduced into the process, which is now rapidly propelling the whole earth toward disaster. One passage in particular expresses the con-

siderable horror with which he views the vanishing
of the primordial order of nature under the thunder-
ing engine of modern technology:

> *It is with the coming of man that a vast hole*
> *seems to open in nature, a vast black whirlpool*
> *spinning faster and faster, consuming flesh,*
> *stones, soil, minerals, sucking down the light-*
> *ning, wrenching power from the atom, until the*
> *ancient sounds of nature are drowned in the*
> *cacophony of something which is no longer*
> *nature, something instead which is loose and*
> *knocking at the world's heart, something de-*
> *monic and no longer planned — escaped, it may*
> *be — spewed out of nature, contending in a*
> *final giant's game against its master.**

Perhaps there is something fundamentally un-
stable about the production of a noosphere anywhere in the universe. It may be that for a planet
on which it happens, the birth of thought is a dark
and ominous cloud which by the time the planet is
subdued becomes a black and terrible storm which
engulfs and ravages it, destroying beyond repair its
long accumulation of evolutionary achievement and
evolutionary potential. Perhaps man, as he crowds
closer and closer together on a shrinking earth and
as the noosphere intensifies and compresses, will

---

*Loren Eiseley, *The Firmament of Time* (New York: Athen-
eum, 1962), p. 123.

inevitably make of it a curse rather than a blessing, death rather than life. Certainly man himself is the one element in all creation over which he was not given, and does not exercise dominion. Possibly the giving of so much power to a finite creature, to give one element of nature dominion over all the rest, may involve so much risk that it should never have been attempted.

Yet this is to speak without hope. It is, it seems to me, to ignore the divine providence which so clearly was involved in producing the noosphere to begin with. In a summary of his thought a year before his death, Teilhard de Chardin, too, takes note of these terrible dangers which seem to be inherent in the compression of the noosphere. But he then sets out to rebut such a pessimistic view of man's future with all his strength. He is sure that the evolutionary process which led to man has a profound and wonderful purpose which will not be thwarted by anything which man will do. Taking portions of two passages, his conviction runs something like this:

For in the course of this unprecedented biological operation of a whole species 'imploding' on itself, we stand at this moment precisely at the sensitive, 'equatorial' point; here the evolution of Homo sapiens, *having hitherto been expansive, is now beginning to become compressive. Inevitably this change of condition, at its* *onset, gave us a kind of vertigo. But enlightened at last by a little more knowledge, we now see that we can face the high pressures of the upper hemisphere, which we have just entered, without fear . . . (Yet) a hominisation of convergence can only end with a paroxysm. Even if consolidated by the final awakening of consciousness of its common destiny, humanity will probably undergo tomorrow, either by its efforts to define and formulate the unity awaiting it, or in the choice and application of the best means to attain it, inner conflicts more violent than any we are familiar with. But since they will develop in a human milieu much more strongly polarised toward the future than we can yet imagine, these phenomena of tension will very likely lose the sterile bitterness peculiar to our present struggles.**

Teilhard's optimism is deeply rooted in his religion. He had a vision of a cosmic energy filling and empowering all matter. For him a creative force has been operative throughout the whole evolutionary process by bringing spirit out of matter and by clothing the earth first in its biosphere and then in its noosphere. This strong sense of the providential character of the past history of the earth is the

---

*Pierre Teilhard de Chardin, *The Appearance of Man* (New York: Harper & Row, 1965), pp. 239 and 258.

ground for hope in the future of man. After the paroxysm of the convergence of the noosphere will come some great transformation of man, an evolutionary leap in the social order, in which the noosphere will become, as Teilhard expresses it, "unanimized" and "amorized." However agonizing the transition may be, I share with Teilhard the hope that the noosphere will then converge upon itself to produce a new form of universal human society and community of the kind which our spaceship status demands. This new society will be as different from that we now know as *Homo sapiens* is different from *Homo habilis*. We cannot really conceive what this will be, since it will be a new creation, nor can we imagine the nature of the events in our future history by which it will be accomplished. Only in the providential character of our past history do we find any assurance that the transformation will be successfully made.

We have seen that the remaining third of this century will be a radically revolutionary period beyond anything that man has known before in his history. We must successfully live through great and terrible times involving tremendous readjustments in human society and the meeting of great challenges to human technological ingenuity and persistence. It is a period which presents not only great dangers to man, but at the same time opportunities to contribute to the welfare of man and his world which will dwarf any he has ever encountered before. To live successfully in a revolutionary period of such magnitude and scope will require great inner resources of faith and courage and a confident hope for man and his future on the earth. Some have offered purely secular grounds for such a hope but I find them unconvincing at best and often quite naive. In a purely secular context, man is really alone in his spaceship as it wends its way on a meaningless journey through the trackless reaches of an impersonal and uncaring universe. In that context it is not possible in the long run to discover any dependable basis for faith in the meaning of the phenomenon of man or for hope in his ultimate destiny. But if in an increasingly secular world men can nevertheless find a basis for hope which is rooted in a transcendent purpose beyond space and time, then, without having to know in advance just how it will be accomplished, men can feel a strong sense of confidence in the ultimate outcome. Such a hope confidently anticipates the same kind of unpredictable and miraculous turns of events in the future which have marked the chances and accidents of man's past history on the planet and brought him to his present remarkable situation. This is as much as can be said about the future of man, but it is enough.

IN APPRECIATION

Each year the Annual Lecture Series at The Claremont Colleges is made possible by a number of generous business and professional leaders in Southern California who sponsor the bringing of a noted lecturer who has something important to say.

The sponsors of the the 1966 lectures by William G. Pollard are as follows:

Earl C. Adams
Robert M. Allan, Jr.
Walter Ames
Mrs. Anna Bing Arnold
Lloyd L. Austin
R. Stanton Avery
Wallace E. Avery
Frederick S. Bale
Joseph A. Ball
Harry M. Bardt
Charles E. Beardsley
Garner A. Beckett
Frank B. Belcher
Harold A. Black
Russell S. Bock
Samuel F. Bowlby
Elliott E. Brainard
Theodore W. Braun
Reid R. Briggs
Roy A. Britt
Ernest A. Bryant, Jr.
Martin J. Burke
Theodore S. Burnett
William B. Carman
Mrs. Perry W. Clark
Dwight L. Clarke
Everett B. Clary
William W. Clary
George W. Cohen
Peter Colefax
Philip Corrin
Honorable E. Avery Crary
William H. Cree, Jr.
Homer D. Crotty
Hugh W. Darling
Robert C. Davidson
M. Philip Davis
Charles Detoy
Charles E. Donnelly
Wesley I. Dumm
Harry L. Dunn
Gabriel C. Duque
Gabriel C. Duque, Jr.
W. Mark Durley
Rollin P. Eckis
Arthur L. Erb
Herman R. Erkes
Knox Farrand
J. E. Fishburn, Jr.
Ross C. Fisher
Philip S. Fogg

Edward T. Foley
Edward C. Freutel, Jr.
F. Daniel Frost
Paul Fussell
Martin Gang
John J. Garland
Henry B. Grandin
Varian S. Green
James C. Greene
Elbert B. Griffith
A. Stevens Halsted, Jr.
Robert P. Hastings
Clyde E. Holley
Charles F. Horne
Jack K. Horton
Preston Hotchkis
Cartwright Hunter
Mrs. Joseph L. Hunter
Earl W. Huntley
Glenn R. Huntoon
George D. Jagels
Felix Juda
C. Clarke Keely
William Scripps Kellogg
Frank L. King
Wayne H. Knight
Oscar T. Lawler
Everett B. Laybourne
Francis H. Lindley
Joseph P. Loeb
Ernest J. Loebbecke
John Warren Loucks
Jonathan B. Lovelace
James E. Ludlam
Louis B. Lundborg
John D. Lusk
August F. Mack, Jr.
A. Calder Mackay
John M. Marble
George R. Martin
Arthur J. McFadden
J. Wallace McKenzie
Harold B. Meloth
Mrs. Victor Montgomery
Ernest L. Mock
Mrs. Andrew Morthland
Coleman W. Morton
Lindley C. Morton
Katsuma Mukaeda
Henry T. Mudd
Dr. Seeley G. Mudd

Elvon Musick
Van Cott Niven
John O'Melveny
Stuart O'Melveny
Judge Isaac Pacht
Mrs. Louise H. Padelford
Austin H. Peck, Jr.
Joseph D. Peeler
Stuart T. Peeler
Morris B. Pendleton
Dr. George Piness
George W. Prince, Jr.
Bruce Renwick
Karl B. Rodi
Iral J. Roller
Mrs. William S. Rosecrans
Joseph H. Russell
Frank H. Schmidt
Richard C. Seaver
William T. Sesnon, Jr.
Leonard A. Shelton
Mrs. Elbert W. Shirk
Mrs. Elden Smith
H. Russell Smith
Roger Bixby Smith
William French Smith
Hugo A. Steinmeyer
Graham L. Sterling, Jr.
Ron Stever
Herbert F. Sturdy
Jesse W. Tapp
Oscar A. Trippet
Clifford Tweter
Max Eddy Utt
Harry Van Luven
Philip K. Verleger
Charles S. Vogel
Richard Von Hagen
Irving D. Walker
Paul D. Walker
Sidney H. Wall
Paul R. Watkins
Gil M. Wayne
Louis M. Welsh
Francis M. Wheat
John L. Wheeler
Sharp Whitmore
George H. Whitney
Richard H. Wolford
Pierce Works
Lewis L. Wright